PLAYALONG FOUR-CHORD SONGBOOK
GUITAR CL

Wise Publications
part of The Music Sales Group

London / New York / Paris / Sydney / Copenhagen / Berlin / Madrid / Tokyo

Published by
Wise Publications
14-15 Berners Street, London W1T 3LJ, UK

Exclusive Distributors:
Music Sales Limited
Distribution Centre, Newmarket Road,
Bury St Edmunds, Suffolk IP33 3YB, UK

Music Sales Pty Limited
20 Resolution Drive,
Caringbah, NSW 2229, Australia

Order No. AM1003695
ISBN 978-1-78038-189-3
This book © Copyright 2011 Wise Publications,
a division of Music Sales Limited.

Printed in the EU

www.musicsales.com

Edited by Adrian Hopkins
Music processed by Paul Ewers Music Design
Cover design by Liz Barrand

America
Guitars: Arthur Dick
Bass: Tom Farncombe
Drums: Chris Baron

The Ballad of John & Yoko
Guitars: Arthur Dick
Bass: Paul Townsend
Drums: Brett Morgan

Beautiful Day
Guitars: Arthur Dick
Bass: Paul Townsend
Drums: Brett Morgan

Brown Eyed Girl
arr. Paul Honey

Common People
Guitars: Arthur Dick

Fairytale Of New York
arr. Paul Honey

Hand In My Pocket
Guitars: Arthur Dick

I Shot The Sheriff
Guitars: Arthur Dick
Bass: Paul Townsend
Drums: Ian Thomas

In My Place
Guitars: Arthur Dick
Bass: Paul Townsend
Drums: Brett Morgan

Jailhouse Rock
Guitars: Arthur Dick

Jamming
Guitars: Arthur Dick

Johnny B Goode
Guitars: Arthur Dick

Late In the Evening
Guitars: Arthur Dick
Bass: Paul Townsend
Drums: Noam Lederman
Brass: The Fullfat Horns

Live Forever
Guitars: Arthur Dick
Bass: Paul Townsend
Drums: Brett Morgan

Naïve
Guitars: Arthur Dick
Bass: Paul Townsend
Drums: Brett Morgan

Rebel Rebel
Guitars: Arthur Dick
Bass: Paul Townsend
Drums: Ian Thomas

Substitute
Guitars: Arthur Dick
Bass: Paul Townsend
Drums: Paul Kemp

Train In Vain
Guitars: Arthur Dick
Bass: Paul Townsend
Drums: Ian Thomas

Wild Wood
Guitars: Arthur Dick

You're Still the One
arr. Paul Honey
Guitars: Arthur Dick

Relative Tuning

The guitar can be tuned with the aid of pitch pipes or dedicated electronic guitar tuners which are available through your local music dealer. If you do not have a tuning device, you can use relative tuning. Estimate the pitch of the 6th string as near as possible to E or at least a comfortable pitch (not too high, as you might break other strings in tuning up). Then, while checking the various positions on the diagram, place a finger from your left hand on the:

5th fret of the E or 6th string and **tune the open A** (or 5th string) to the note Ⓐ

5th fret of the A or 5th string and **tune the open D** (or 4th string) to the note Ⓓ

5th fret of the D or 4th string and **tune the open G** (or 3rd string) to the note Ⓖ

4th fret of the G or 3rd string and **tune the open B** (or 2nd string) to the note Ⓑ

5th fret of the B or 2nd string and **tune the open E** (or 1st string) to the note Ⓔ

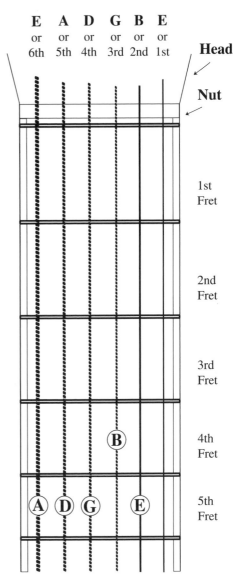

Reading Chord Boxes

Chord boxes are diagrams of the guitar neck viewed head upwards, face on as illustrated. The top horizontal line is the nut, unless a higher fret number is indicated, the others are the frets.

The vertical lines are the strings, starting from E (or 6th) on the left to E (or 1st) on the right.

The black dots indicate where to place your fingers.

Strings marked with an O are played open, not fretted. Strings marked with an X should not be played.

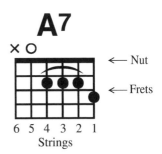

The curved bracket indicates a 'barre' - hold down the strings under the bracket with your first finger, using your other fingers to fret the remaining notes.

N.C. = No Chord.

5

America

Words & Music by
Johnny Borrell & Andy Burrows

C   D   G   Am

Capo seventh fret

Intro

| C D | G C | C D | G C |
| C | G C | C D | G C ‖

Verse 1

        C   D
        What a drag it is,
    G   C
        The shape I'm in.
    D
    I go out somewhere,
            G   C
    Then I come home again.
    C   D
        I light a cigarette,
    G   C
        'Cause I can't get no sleep.

    There's nothing on the TV,
            D
    No - thing on the radio,
            G   C
    That means that much to me.

Chorus 1

        C   D
        All my life,
    G   C
        Watching A - merica.
                D
    All my life,
    G   C
        There's panic in A-merica.

cont.

  Am   **D**
  Oh, oh, oh, oh!

G   **C**
  There's trouble in A - merica.

Am   **D** **G**
  Oh, oh, oh, oh.

Verse 2

  C   **D**
  Yester - day was easy,

G   **C**
Happiness came and went.

     D
I got the movie script,

    G   **C**
But I don't know what it meant.

C   **D**
  I light a cigarette,

    G   **C**
Cause I can't get no sleep.

There's nothing on the TV,

    D
No - thing on the radio,

   G   **C**
That means that much to me.

Nothing on the TV,

    D   **G**   **C**
No - thing on the radio, that I can believe in.

Chorus 2

  C   **D**
  All my life,

G   **C**
  Watching A - merica.

    D
All my life,

G   **C**
  There's panic in A - merica.

cont.

  Am   D
   Oh, oh, oh, oh!
  G   C
   There's trouble in A - merica.
  Am   D
   Oh, oh, oh, oh!
  G   C
   There's trouble in A - merica.
  Am   D G
   Oh, oh, oh, oh!

Link | C D | G | C D | G |

Verse 3

  C   D
   Yester - day was easy
  G   C
  Yes, I got the news.
  C   D
   Oh, when you get it straight,
      G   C
  You stand up you just can't lose.
       D
  Give you my confidence,
  G   C
  All my faith in life.
    C
  Don't stand me up,
    D
  Don't let me down, no,
  G   C
  I need you tonight.
    C D
  To hold me,
  G   C
   Say you'll be here.

<pre>
                 C   D
cont.   And hold me,
          G   C
             Say you'll be here.
                 C   D
          And hold me,
          G   C
          Say you'll be here.
          C   D   G   C
          Hold.

                 Am   D
Chorus 3   All my life
          G   C
             I'm watching A - merica
          Am   D
             All my life,
          G   C
             There's panic in A - merica.
          Am   D
             Oh, oh, oh,   oh!
          G   C
             She's lost in A - merica.
          Am   D   G   C
             Oh, oh, oh,   oh.
                           Am   D   G   C
          Tell me how does it feel?
                           Am   D   G   C
          Tell me how does it feel?
                           Am   D   G
          Tell me how does it feel?
</pre>

Outro

<pre>
| C D | G C | C D | G C |

| C D | G C | C D | G C |

| G   C | G   C | G   C ‖
</pre>

The Ballad Of John And Yoko

Words & Music by
John Lennon & Paul McCartney

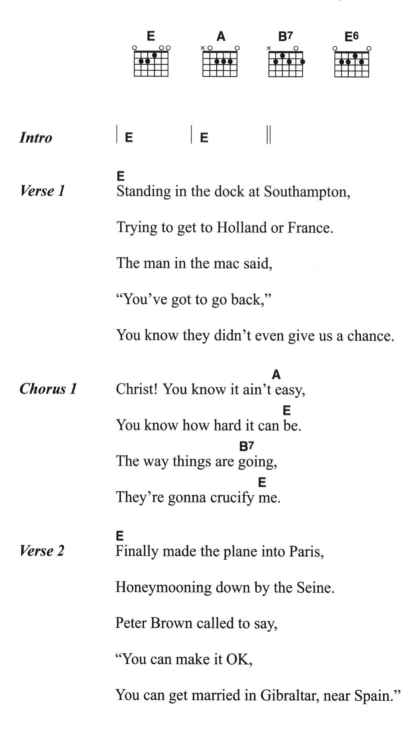

E   **A**   **B7**   **E6**

Intro | E | E ||

Verse 1

E
Standing in the dock at Southampton,

Trying to get to Holland or France.

The man in the mac said,

"You've got to go back,"

You know they didn't even give us a chance.

Chorus 1

                A
Christ! You know it ain't easy,

               E
You know how hard it can be.

         B7
The way things are going,

          E
They're gonna crucify me.

Verse 2

E
Finally made the plane into Paris,

Honeymooning down by the Seine.

Peter Brown called to say,

"You can make it OK,

You can get married in Gibraltar, near Spain."

Chorus 2   As Chorus 1

                   E

Verse 3   Drove from Paris to the Amsterdam Hilton,

                Talking in our beds for a week.

                The newspeople said,

                "Say what you doing in bed?"

                I said, "We're only trying to get us some peace."

Chorus 3   As Chorus 1

                   A

Bridge   Saving up your money for a rainy day,

                Giving all your clothes to charity.

                Last night the wife said,

                "Oh boy, when you're dead,

                   B7

                You don't take nothing with you but your soul."

                Think!

                   E

Verse 4   Made a lightning trip to Vienna,

                Eating chocolate cake in a bag.

                The newspapers said,

                "She's gone to his head,

                They look just like two gurus in drag."

                             A

Chorus 4   Christ! You know it ain't easy,

                               E

                You know how hard it can be.

                   B7

                The way things are going,

                   E

                They're gonna crucify me.

Verse 5

E
Caught the early plane back to London,

Fifty acorns tied in a sack.

The men from the press said,

"We wish you success,

It's good to have the both of you back."

Chorus 5

A
Christ! You know it ain't easy,
E
You know how hard it can be.
B7
The way things are going,
E
They're gonna crucify me.

Coda

B7
The way things are going,
E
They're gonna crucify me.

| B7 | B7 | E | E6 ‖

Beautiful Day

Words by Bono
Music by U2

D   Em   G   C

Capo seventh fret

Intro ‖: D   Em G │ C   │ G   D │ D   :‖

Verse 1
                              D   Em G
The heart is a bloom,
C   G   D
  Shoots up through the stony ground.
                     Em G
But there's no room,
C   G   D
  No space to rent in this   town.
                Em G
You're out of luck,
C   G   D
  And the reason that you had to care.
                Em G
The traffic is stuck,
C   G   D
  And you're not moving anywhere.
                    Em G
You thought you'd found a friend
C   G   D
  To take you out of this place,
             Em   G C   G   D
Someone you could lend a hand in return for grace.

Chorus 1
                  D   Em G C
It's a beautiful day,
G   D
  The sky falls, you feel like
               Em G C
It's a beautiful day,
       G   D
Don't let it get away.

Verse 2

                     D   Em G
You're on the road
 C   G   D
But you've got no destination.
                 Em G
You're in the mud
 C   G   D
In the maze of her imagination.
                 Em G
You love this town____
 C G   D
Even if that doesn't ring true.
            Em G
You've been all   over,
 C   G   D
And it's been all over you.

Chorus 2

                    D   Em G   C
It's a beautiful day,
 G   D
Don't let it get away.
               Em G   C G   D
It's a beautiful day.
 G   C G   D
Touch me,   take me to that other place,
 G   C G   D
Teach me,   I know I'm not a hopeless case.

Link | D Em G | C | G   D | D ||

Bridge

 C
See the world in green and blue:
 G
See China right in front of you,
 C
See the canyons broken by cloud,
 G
See the tuna fleets clearing the sea out,
 C
See the Bedouin fires at night,
 G
See the oil fields at first light and,

cont.

C
   See the bird with a leaf in her mouth;

G   D
   After the flood all the colours came out.

D   G   D
Day,—— day.——

Chorus 3

                    D   Em G   C
   It was a beautiful day,

          G   D
   Don't let it get away;

              Em C   G   D
Beautiful day.——————

G   C G   D
Touch me,   take me to that other place,

G   C   G   D
Rea - ch me, I know I'm not a hopeless case.

Coda

                   D   Em G   C
What you don't have you don't need it now,

          G   D
What you don't know you can feel it somehow;

                   Em G   C
What you don't have you don't need it now,

       G   D
Don't need it now,

                   Em G   C   G   D
It was a beautiful day.——————

| D Em G | C | G   D | D |

| (D) (Em) (G) | (C) | (G)   (D) | (D) |

| (D) (Em) (G) | (C)   ‖

Brown Eyed Girl

Words & Music by
Van Morrison

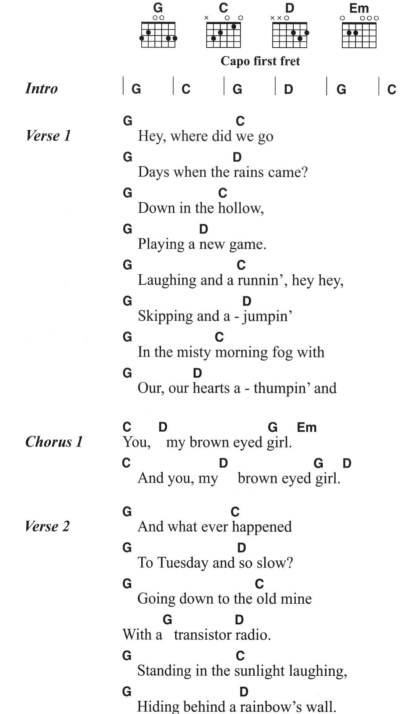

Capo first fret

Intro | G | C | G | D | G | C | G | D ‖

Verse 1

G   C
Hey, where did we go

G   D
Days when the rains came?

G   C
Down in the hollow,

G   D
Playing a new game.

G   C
Laughing and a runnin', hey hey,

G   D
Skipping and a - jumpin'

G   C
In the misty morning fog with

G   D
Our, our hearts a - thumpin' and

Chorus 1

C   D   G   Em
You,   my brown eyed girl.

C   D   G D
And you, my   brown eyed girl.

Verse 2

G   C
And what ever happened

G   D
To Tuesday and so slow?

G   C
Going down to the old mine

            G   D
With a   transistor radio.

G   C
Standing in the sunlight laughing,

G   D
Hiding behind a rainbow's wall.

cont.

 G   C
  Slipping and a - sliding
 G   D
  All along the waterfall with

Chorus 2

 C D   G Em
 You, my brown eyed girl.
 C   D   G D
  You, my brown eyed girl.

           G
 Do you remember when we used to sing
     C   G   D
 Sha la la la la la la, la la la la de da.
       G   C
 Just like that, sha la la la la la la,
 G   D   (G)
 La la la la de da, la de da.

Link

| G | G | G | G | G | C | G | D ‖

Verse 3

 G   C
  So hard to find my way
 G   D
  Now that I'm all on my own
 G   C
  I saw you just the other day
 G   D
  My, how you have grown
 G   C
  Cast my memory back there, Lord
 G   D
  Sometimes I'm overcome thinkin' about it
 G   C
  Makin' love in the green grass
 G   D
  Behind the stadium with

Chorus 3

 C D   G Em
 You, my brown eyed girl
 C   D   G D
  And you, my brown eyed girl.
       G
 Do you remember when we used to sing
  G   C   G   D
‖: Sha la la la la la la, la la la la de da.
 G   C   G   D
 Sha la la la la la la, la la la la de da, :‖ *Repeat ad lib. to fade*

Common People

Words by Jarvis Cocker
Music by Jarvis Cocker, Nick Banks, Russell Senior, Candida Doyle & Stephen Mackey

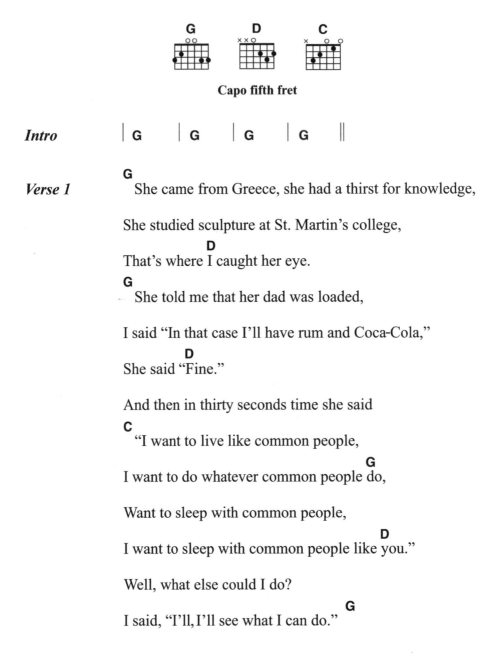

Capo fifth fret

Intro | G | G | G | G ||

Verse 1

G
   She came from Greece, she had a thirst for knowledge,

She studied sculpture at St. Martin's college,
      D
That's where I caught her eye.
G
  She told me that her dad was loaded,

I said "In that case I'll have rum and Coca-Cola,"
      D
She said "Fine."

And then in thirty seconds time she said
C
  "I want to live like common people,
           G
I want to do whatever common people do,

Want to sleep with common people,
             D
I want to sleep with common people like you."

Well, what else could I do?
            G
I said, "I'll, I'll see what I can do."

Verse 2

(G)
I took her to a supermarket,

                                                  D
I don't know why but I had to start it somewhere, so it started there.

G
  I said "Pretend you've got no money."

                                                       D
She just laughed and said "Oh, you're so funny." I said "Yeah?

Well I can't see anyone else smiling in here.

            C
Are you sure you want to live like common people,

                         G
You want to see whatever common people see,

You want to sleep with common people,

                         D
You want to sleep with common people like me?"

                                 G
But she didn't understand, she just smiled and held my hand.

Verse 3

Rent a flat above a shop, cut your hair and get a job,

           D
Smoke some fags and play some pool, pretend you never went to school,

         G
But still you'll never get it right 'cause when you're laid in bed at night

       D
Watching 'roaches climb the wall,

If you called your dad he could stop it all, yeah.

C
  You'll never live like common people,

                      G
You'll never do whatever common people do.

You'll never fail like common people,

                     D
You'll never watch your life slide out of view,

And then dance and drink and screw

            G
Because there's nothing else to do.

Instrumental ‖: G | G | G | G |

             | D | D | D | D   :‖

Verse 4
    C
  Sing along with the common people,

                G
Sing along and it might just get you through.

Laugh along with the common people,

                    D
Laugh along even though they're laughing at you,

And the stupid things that you do,

            G
Because you think that poor is cool.

Verse 5   Like a dog lying in the corner,

They will bite you and never warn you,

  D
Look out, they'll tear your insides out,

G
  'Cause everybody hates a tourist,

                  D
Especially one who thinks it's all such a laugh,

And the chip stains and grease will come out in the bath.

      C
You will never understand how it feels to live your life

      G
With no meaning or control and with nowhere left to go.

      D
You are amazed that they exist,

                  G
And they burn so bright whilst you can only wonder why.

Verse 6   As Verse 3

Outro | **G** | **G** | **G** | **G** ||

            (G)
‖: Want to live with common people like you. :‖ *Play 7 times*

‖: Oh, la, la, la, la. :‖   *Play 4 times*

Oh yeah.

Jamming

Words & Music by
Bob Marley

Bm7   E   G   F#m

Intro   ‖: Bm7 | E | G | F#m   :‖

Chorus 1
        Bm7   **E**
We're jamming,
  G   **F#m**
  I wanna jam it with you,
        Bm7   **E**
We're jamming, jamming,
     G   **F#m**
And I hope you like jamming too.

Verse 1
          Bm7   **E**
Ain't no rules, ain't no vow,
       Bm7   **E**
We can do it anyhow,
  G   **F#m**
I-and-I will see you through,
         Bm7   **E**
'Cause every day we pay the price
       Bm7   **E**
With a little sacrifice,
  G   **F#m**
Jamming till the jam is through.

Chorus 2
        Bm7   **E**
We're jamming,
            G   **F#m**
To think that jamming was a thing of the past,
     Bm7   **E**
We're jamming,
  G   **F#m**
And I hope this jam is gonna last.

Verse 2

Bm⁷   E
No bullet can stop us now,

       Bm⁷   E
We neither beg nor we won't bow,

G   F♯m
Neither can be bought nor sold.

    Bm⁷   E
We all defend the right,

       Bm⁷   E
Jah Jah children must unite,

     G   F♯m
Your life is worth much more than gold.

Chorus 3

       Bm⁷
We're jamming,

      E
(Jamming, jamming, jamming,)

        G   F♯m
And we're jamming in the name of the Lord,

       Bm⁷
We're jamming,

      E
(Jamming, jamming, jamming,)

     G   F♯m
We're jamming right straight from Jah.

Bridge

Bm⁷   E
     Holy Mount Zion,

Bm⁷   E
     Holy Mount Zion.

Bm⁷ N.C.
     Jah sitteth in Mount Zion

Bm⁷ N.C.
     And rules all Creation.

Chorus 4

       Bm⁷
Yeah, we're jamming,

E   Bm⁷
(Pop-choo), pop-choo-wa-wa,

Bm⁷
    We're jamming (pop-choo-wa), see?

G   F♯m
    I wanna jam it with you.

      Bm⁷
We're jamming,

         E
(Jamming, jamming, jamming,)

  G   **F♯m**
I'm jammed, I hope you're jamming too.

Verse 3

Bm⁷   **E**   **Bm⁷**   **E**
Jam's about my pride and truth I cannot hide

G   **F♯m**
  To keep you satisfied.

    Bm⁷   **E**   **Bm⁷**   **E**
True love that now exist is the love I can't resist

   G   **F♯m**
So   jam by my side.

Chorus 5

         Bm⁷
‖: Yeah, we're jamming,

      E
(Jamming, jamming, jamming)

G   **F♯m**
  I wanna jam it with you.

    Bm⁷
We're jamming, we're jamming,

We're jamming, we're jamming,

    E
We're jamming, we're jamming,

We're jamming, we're jamming,

G   **F♯m**
  Hope you like jamming too. :‖ *Repeat to end with ad lib. vocals*

Fairytale Of New York

Words & Music by
Shane MacGowan & Jem Finer

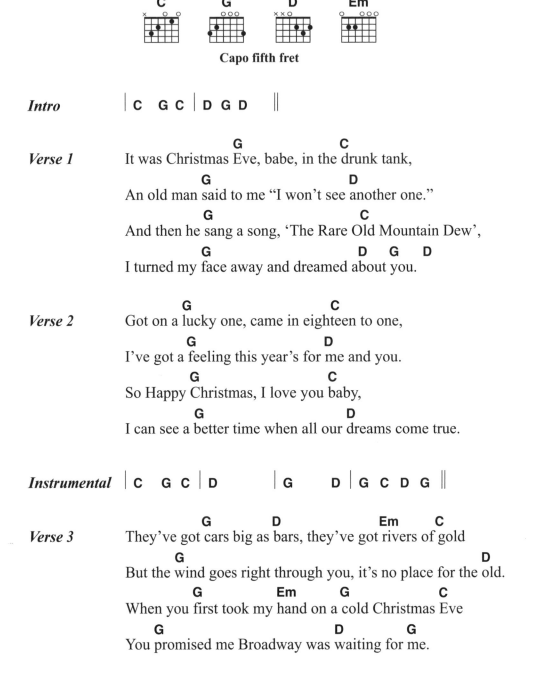

C   G   D   Em

Capo fifth fret

Intro | C   G C | D G D ||

Verse 1
                         G   C
It was Christmas Eve, babe, in the drunk tank,
                 G   D
An old man said to me "I won't see another one."
                   G   C
And then he sang a song, 'The Rare Old Mountain Dew',
                G   D   G   D
I turned my face away and dreamed about you.

Verse 2
               G   C
Got on a lucky one, came in eighteen to one,
                G   D
I've got a feeling this year's for me and you.
                G   C
So Happy Christmas, I love you baby,
                G   D
I can see a better time when all our dreams come true.

Instrumental | C   G C | D | G   D | G C D G ||

Verse 3
                G   D   Em   C
They've got cars big as bars, they've got rivers of gold
                G   D
But the wind goes right through you, it's no place for the old.
                G   Em   G   C
When you first took my hand on a cold Christmas Eve
                G   D   G
You promised me Broadway was waiting for me.

Verse 4
              G   D

You were handsome, you were pretty, queen of New York City.

      G   C   D   G

When the band finished playing, they howled out for more.

  G   D

Sinatra was swinging, all the drunks they were singing,

      G   C   D   G

We kissed on a corner then danced through the night.

Chorus 1
            C   Em D   G   Em

And the boys from the NYPD   choir were singing 'Galway Bay'

      G   C   D   G

And the bells were ringin' out for Christmas Day.

Link 1 | G D Em C | G   D | G Em G C | G   D G ‖

Verse 5
            G   D

You're a bum, you're a punk, you're an old slut on junk

      G   C   D   G

Lying there almost dead on a drip in that bed.

    G   D

You scumbag, you maggot, you cheap lousy faggot,

      G   C   D   G

Happy Christmas your arse, I pray God it's our last.

Chorus 2   As Chorus 1

Link 2 | G | C | G   C | D G D ‖

Verse 6
            G   C

I could have been someone, well so could anyone.

          G   D

You took my dreams from me when I first found you.

         G   C

I kept them with me, babe, I put them with my own,

            G   C   D   G

I can't make it   all alone, I've built my dreams around you.

Chorus 3   As Chorus 1

Hand In My Pocket

Words by Alanis Morissette
Music by Alanis Morissette & Glen Ballard

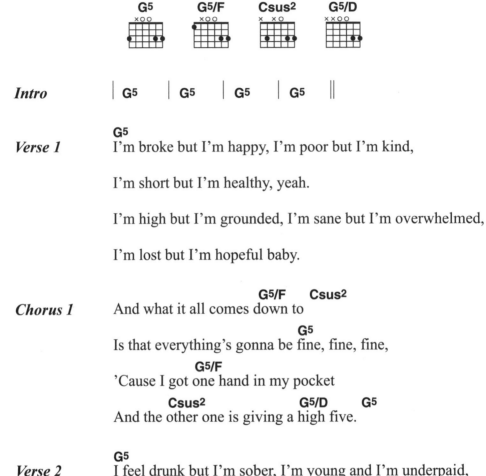

Intro | G5 | G5 | G5 | G5 ||

Verse 1

G5
I'm broke but I'm happy, I'm poor but I'm kind,

I'm short but I'm healthy, yeah.

I'm high but I'm grounded, I'm sane but I'm overwhelmed,

I'm lost but I'm hopeful baby.

Chorus 1

                                 G5/F   Csus2
And what it all comes down to

                             G5
Is that everything's gonna be fine, fine, fine,

              G5/F
'Cause I got one hand in my pocket

          Csus2   G5/D   G5
And the other one is giving a high five.

Verse 2

G5
I feel drunk but I'm sober, I'm young and I'm underpaid,

I'm tired but I'm working, yeah.

I care but I'm restless, I'm here but I'm really gone,

I'm wrong and I'm sorry baby.

Chorus 2

                       G5/F   **Csus2**
And what it all comes down to

                          G5
Is that everything's gonna be quite all right,

       G5/F
'Cause I've got one hand in my pocket

  Csus2   **G5/D**   **G5**
And the other one is flicking a cigarette.

Solo | G5 | G5 | G5 | G5 | G5 | G5 | G5 | G5 ||

Chorus 3

                       G5/F   **Csus2**
And what it all comes down to

                          G5
Is that I haven't got it all figured out just yet,

       G5/F
'Cause I've got one hand in my pocket

  Csus2   **G5/D**   **G5**
And the other one is giving a peace sign.

Verse 3

G5
I'm free but I'm focused, I'm green but I'm wise,

I'm hard but I'm friendly baby.

I'm sad but I'm laughing, I'm brave but I'm chickenshit,

I'm sick but I'm pretty baby.

Chorus 4

                     G5/F   **Csus2**
And what it all boils down to

                       G5
Is that no one's got it figured out just yet.

     G5/F
But I've got one hand in my pocket

  Csus2   **G5/D**   **G5**
And the other one is playing a piano.

Chorus 5

                   G5/F   **Csus2**
And what it all comes down to my friends

                 G5
Is that every thing is just fine, fine, fine,

       G5/F
'Cause I've got one hand in my pocket

  Csus2   **G5/D**   **G5**
And the other one is hailing a taxi cab.

I Shot The Sheriff

Words & Music by
Bob Marley

Gm   Cm7   E♭maj7   Dm7

Chorus 1

Gm   Cm7   Gm
I shot the sheriff,   but I did not shoot the deputy.

                 Cm7   Gm
I shot the sheriff,   but I did not shoot the deputy.

Verse 1

E♭maj7 Dm7   Gm
All   around in my home town

E♭maj7   Dm7   Gm
They're trying to track me down.

    E♭maj7   Dm7   Gm
They say they want to bring me in guilty,

        E♭maj7   Dm7 Gm
For the killing of a deputy,

         E♭maj7 Dm7 Gm   N.C.
For the life of a depu-ty, but I say:

Chorus 2

Gm   Cm7   Gm
I shot the sheriff,   but I swear it was in self-defence.

                 Cm7   Gm
I shot the sheriff,   and they say it is a capital offence.

Verse 2

E♭maj7   Dm7   Gm
      Sheriff John Brown always hated me,

E♭maj7 Dm7 Gm
For what I don't know.

E♭maj7   Dm7   Gm
And every time that I plant a seed,

        E♭maj7 Dm7 Gm
He said, "Kill it before it grows,"

        E♭maj7 Dm7 Gm   N.C.
He said, "Kill it before it grows." I say:

Chorus 3

Gm   Cm7   Gm
I shot the sheriff,   but I swear it was in self-defence.

                    Cm7   Gm
I shot the sheriff,   but I swear it was in self-defence.

Verse 3

E♭maj7 Dm7   Gm
Freedom came my way one day,

E♭maj7 Dm7   Gm
  And I started out of town, yeah.

E♭maj7   Dm7   Gm
  All of a sudden I see Sheriff John Brown,

E♭maj7 Dm7   Gm
      Aimin' to shoot me down.

    E♭maj7 Dm7   Gm   ⌢· N.C.
So I shot,   I shot him down, and I say:

Chorus 4

Gm   Cm7   Gm
I shot the sheriff,   but I did not shoot the deputy.

                   Cm7   Gm
I shot the sheriff,   but I did not shoot the deputy.

Verse 4

E♭maj7 Dm7   Gm
      Reflexes got the better of me

E♭maj7 Dm7   Gm
      And what is to be must be.

E♭maj7   Dm7   Gm
      Everyday the bucket goes to the well,

E♭maj7   Dm7   Gm
      But one day the bottom will drop out,

E♭maj7   Dm7   Gm   N.C.
      Yes, one day the bottom will drop out. I say:

Chorus 5

Gm   Cm7   Gm
I shot the sheriff,   but I did not shoot the deputy.

                   Cm7   Gm
I shot the sheriff,   but I did not shoot no deputy, oh no.

Outro   ‖: E♭maj7 | Dm7 | Gm   :‖ *Play 8 times to fade*

In My Place

Words & Music by
Guy Berryman, Chris Martin, Jon Buckland & Will Champion

G   D   Em   C

Capo second fret

Intro | 2 bars drums ‖

‖: G | D | G   Em | D   :‖

Verse 1

     G   D   G
In my place, in my place were lines that I couldn't change
        Em   D
I was lost, oh yeah.
     G   D   G
And I was lost, I was lost, crossed lines I shouldn't have crossec
        Em   D   D
I was lost, oh yeah.

Chorus 1

     C   G   D   C
Yeah, how long must you wait for it?
          G   D   C
Yeah, how long must you pay for it?
          G   D   C
Yeah, how long must you wait for it?
     D
     Ah, for it?

Link | G | D | G   Em | D   ‖

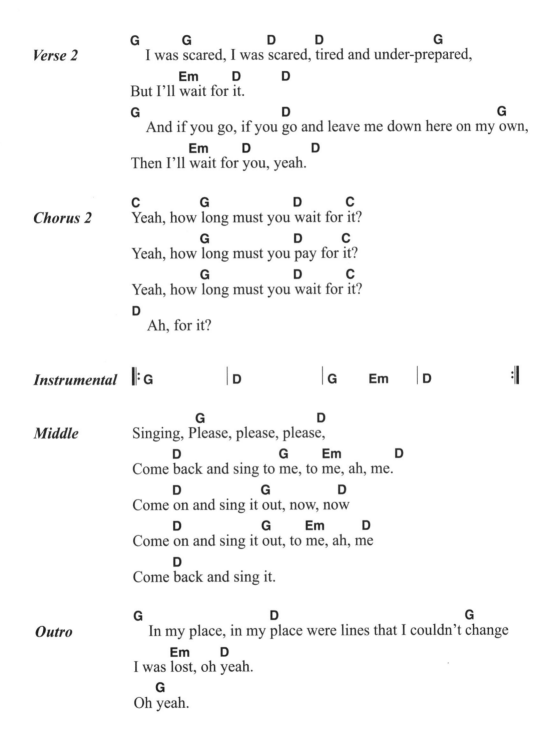

Verse 2

```
  G       G           D     D                G
  I was scared, I was scared, tired and under-prepared,
          Em    D     D
  But I'll wait for it.
  G                   D                        G
    And if you go, if you go and leave me down here on my own,
          Em    D     D
  Then I'll wait for you, yeah.
```

Chorus 2

```
  C       G           D     C
  Yeah, how long must you wait for it?
          G           D     C
  Yeah, how long must you pay for it?
          G           D      C
  Yeah, how long must you wait for it?
  D
    Ah, for it?
```

Instrumental

```
‖: G            | D          | G     Em  | D           :‖
```

Middle

```
          G               D
  Singing, Please, please, please,
          D           G     Em      D
  Come back and sing to me, to me, ah, me.
          D           G         D
  Come on and sing it out, now, now
          D           G     Em      D
  Come on and sing it out, to me, ah, me
              D
  Come back and sing it.
```

Outro

```
  G                   D                        G
    In my place, in my place were lines that I couldn't change
          Em    D
  I was lost, oh yeah.
      G
  Oh yeah.
```

Jailhouse Rock

Words & Music by
Jerry Leiber & Mike Stoller

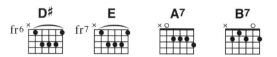

Tune guitar down one semitone

Intro | D♯ | E   D♯ | E   D♯ ||

Verse 1

E
Warden threw a party in the County jail:
D♯   E
   The prison band was there, they began to wail;
D♯   E
   The band was jumpin' and the joint began to swing,
D♯   E   N.C.
   You should've heard those knocked-out jail-birds sing.

Chorus 1

     A7   E
Let's rock, everybody let's rock.
     B7   A7
Everybody in the whole cell block
     E
Was dancing to the jailhouse rock.

Verse 2

D♯ E
   Spider Murphy played his tenor saxophone,
D♯ E
   Little Joe was blowin' on the slide trombone.
D♯   E
   The drummer boy from Illinois went crash boom bang,
D♯   E   N.C.
   The whole rhythm section was a purple gang.

Chorus 2   As Chorus 1

Verse 3

      D♯ E
Number forty seven said to number three,

      D♯   E
"You're the cutest jail-bird I ever did see.

      D♯   E
I sure would be delighted with your company,

      D♯   E   N.C.
C'mon and do the jailhouse rock with me."

Chorus 3

      A7   E
Let's rock, everybody let's rock.

      B7   A7
Everybody in the whole cell block

      E
Was dancing to the jailhouse rock.

Rock, rock!

Guitar Solo | A7 | A7 | E | E | B7 | A7 | E | E ‖

Verse 4

      D♯ E
Sad sack was sitting on a block of stone,

      D♯   E
Way over in the corner weeping all alone.

      D♯   E
The warden said, "Hey, Buddy, don't you be no square:

      D♯   E N.C.
If you can't find a partner use a wooden chair."

Chorus 4   As Chorus 1

Verse 5

      D♯ E
Shifty Henry said, "Hey Bugs, for Heaven's sake,

      D♯   E
No-one's looking out, now's our chance to make a break."

      D♯ E
Bugsy turned to Shifty and he said, "Nix, nix,

      D♯ E   N.C.
I wanna stick around awhile and get my kicks."

Chorus 5   As Chorus 1

Outro   ‖: D♯ E
                Dancing to the jailhouse rock. :‖ *Repeat to fade*

Johnny B. Goode

Words & Music by
Chuck Berry

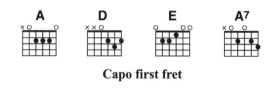

Capo first fret

Intro | A | A | A | A |

             | D | D | A | A |

             | E | E | A | A ||

Verse 1
      A
Deep down in Louisiana, close to New Orleans,

Way back up in the woods among the evergreens,
     D
There stood a log cabin made of earth and wood,
     A
Where lived a country boy named Johnny B. Goode,
     E
Who never ever learned to read or write so well,
     A
But he could play a guitar just like a-ringing a bell.

Chorus 1
     A
Go! Go! Go Johnny, go,

Go! Go Johnny, go,
D
Go! Go Johnny, go,
A
Go! Go Johnny, go,
E   **A**
Go! Johnny B. Goode.

Verse 2
            A
He used to carry his guitar in a gunny sack,

Go sit beneath the tree by the railroad track.
   D
Old engineer in the train sittin' in the shade,
A
Strummin' with the rhythm that the drivers made.
     E
The people passin' by, they would stop and say,
   A
"Oh my, but that little country boy could play."

Chorus 2   As Chorus 1

Guitar solo ‖: A   N.C. | A   N.C. | A N.C. A N.C. | A |

              | D | D | A | A |

              | E | E | A | A :‖

Verse 3
           A
His mother told him, "Someday you will be a man,

And you will be the leader of a big ol' band.
D
Many people coming from miles around,
   A
To hear you play your music till the sun goes down.
E
Maybe someday your name'll be in lights,
    A
Saying 'Johnny B. Goode tonight.'"

Chorus 3   As Chorus 1

Coda | A A⁷ ‖

35

Live Forever

Words & Music by
Noel Gallagher

G   D   C   Em

Verse 1

    G   D
Maybe I don't really want to know

          C
How your garden grows,

           D
I just want to fly.

G   D
Lately, did you ever feel the pain

         C
In the morning rain

                   D   Em
As it soaks you to the bone.

Chorus 1

                D
Maybe I just want to fly,

                      C
I want to live, I don't want to die,

Maybe I just want to breathe,

         D   Em
Maybe I just don't believe.

                  D
Maybe you're the same as me,

                 C
We see things they'll never see,

You and I are gonna live forever.

Verse 2

        G   **D**
I said maybe I don't really want to know

          C
How your garden grows,

             D
I just want to fly.

G   **D**
Lately, did you ever feel the pain

         C
In the morning rain

                 D   **Em**
As it soaks you to the bone.

Chorus 2

                 D
Maybe I will never be

             C
All the things I want to be,

             C
But now is not the time to cry,

     D   **Em**
Now's the time to find out why

                D
I think you're the same as me,

                C
We see things they'll never see,

You and I are gonna live forever.

Guitar solo

G	D	C	C D
G	D	C	C D
Em	D	C	C D
Em	D	C	C	C

Verse 3   As Verse 1

Chorus 3   As Chorus 1

           C
‖: Gonna live forever. :‖   *Play 6 times*

                Play 8 times

Guitar solo   ‖: C | C   :‖ C   ‖

Late In The Evening

Words & Music by
Paul Simon

| F | B♭ | C |

Intro | F | F | F | F | B♭ | B♭ | F | F |

| B♭ | B♭ | F | F | C | C | F | F |

Verse 1
      B♭
The first thing I remember

I was lying in my bed,

I couldn't have been no more
                    F
Than one or two.
     B♭
And I remember there's a radio

Coming from the room next door

And my mother laughed
              F
The way some ladies do
        C
When it's late in the evening
                    F
And the music's seeping through.

Verse 2
      B♭
The next thing I remember

I am walking down the street:

I'm feeling all right,
                          F
I'm with my boys, I'm with my troops, yeah.

cont.

       B♭
And down along the avenue

Some guys were shooting pool

And I heard the sound

       F
Of a capella groups, yeah,

      C
Singing late in the evening

             F
And all the girls out on the stoops, yeah.

Verse 3

      B♭
Then I learned to play some lead guitar.

I was underage in this funky bar

                  F
And I stepped outside to smoke myself a 'J',

  B♭
And when I came back to the room

Everybody just seemed to move

               F
And I turned my amp up loud and I began to play,

   C
And it was late in the evening

         F
And I blew that room   away.

Link

B♭	**B♭**	**F**	**F**	**B♭**	**B♭**	
F	**F**	**C**	**C**	**F**	**F**	‖

Verse 4

  B♭
The first thing I remember

When you came into my life:

I said, I'm gonna get that girl

        F
No matter what I do.

cont.

        B♭
Well I guess I'd been in love before,

And once or twice I been on the floor,

But I never loved no-one
        F
The way that I loved you.
     C
And it was late in the evening
        F
And all the music seeping through.

Coda
   | *Drums for 4 bars*   ‖

F	F	F	F	B♭	B♭	F	F	
B♭	B♭	F	F	C	C	F	F	
F	F	F	F	F	F	F	F	

To fade

Naïve

Words & Music by
Luke Pritchard, Hugh Harris, Max Rafferty & Paul Garred

Em   C   D   G

Capo fourth fret

Intro | Em | C | D | G   D ‖

Verse 1
       Em   C
I'm not sayin' it was your fault,
                               D
Although you could have done more.
          G   D   Em
Oh, you're so na - ïve yet so.
                  C
How could this be done
                        D
By such a smiling sweet - heart?
      G   D   Em
Oh, and your sweet and pretty face,
                 C
It's such an ugly word
                    D
For something so beauti - ful.
      G   D
Oh, that everytime I look inside.

Chorus 1
   C   G   D   C
I know, she knows that I'm   not fond of asking.
                          G
True or false it may be,
                   D   C
Oh, she's still out to get me.
                        Em   D   C
And I know, she knows that I'm not fond of asking.
                          G
True or false it may be,
              D
She's still out to get me.

Link 1 | C | C   ‖

Verse 2

```
Em                         C
   I may say it was your fault,
                                        D
Because I know you could have done more.
        G     D       Em
Oh you're so na - ïve yet so.
                    C
How could this be done
                      D
By such a smiling sweet - heart?
     G                D          Em
Oh, and your sweet and pretty face,

It's such an ugly word
C                           D
   For something so beauti - ful,
      G           D
That everytime I look inside.
```

Chorus 2   As Chorus 1

Interlude | Em | Em | Em | C |

                | Em | Em | D | D   ‖

Verse 3

```
Em                      C
   So how could this be done
                      D
By such a smiling sweet - heart?
     G        D       Em
Oh you're so na - ïve yet so.

Such an ugly thing
C                           D
   For someone so beauti - ful,
      G              D
But everytime you're on his side.
```

Chorus 3   As Chorus 1

Outro   **C   D   Em**
                             G   **C   D   Em**
                Just don't let me down.
                             G
                Just don't let me down

                     C   D   Em
                ‖: Hold on to your kite,
                             G   **C   D   Em**
                Just don't let me down.
                             G
                Just don't let me down :‖

                C   D   Em
                Hold on to this kite,
                             G   **C   D   Em**
                Just don't let me down.

                Just don't let me down.

Rebel Rebel

Words & Music by
David Bowie

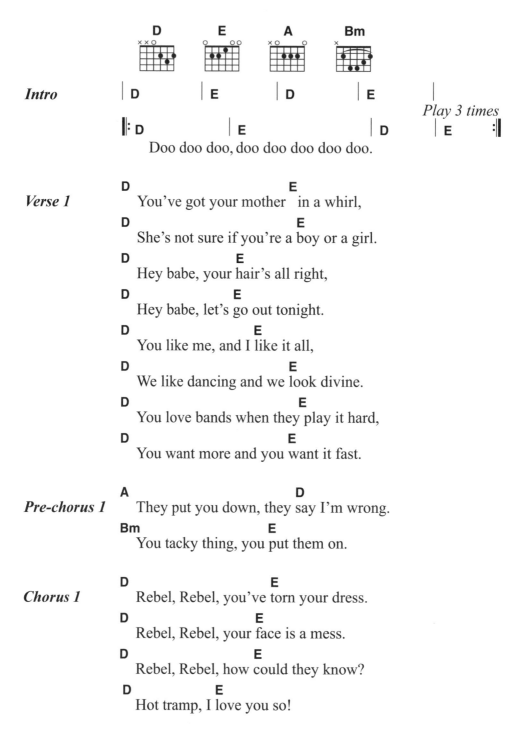

Intro

| D | E | D | E | |

Play 3 times

‖: D | E | D | E :‖

Doo doo doo, doo doo doo doo doo.

Verse 1

D   E
You've got your mother   in a whirl,

D   E
She's not sure if you're a boy or a girl.

D   E
Hey babe, your hair's all right,

D   E
Hey babe, let's go out tonight.

D   E
You like me, and I like it all,

D   E
We like dancing and we look divine.

D   E
You love bands when they play it hard,

D   E
You want more and you want it fast.

Pre-chorus 1

A   D
They put you down, they say I'm wrong.

Bm   E
You tacky thing, you put them on.

Chorus 1

D   E
Rebel, Rebel, you've torn your dress.

D   E
Rebel, Rebel, your face is a mess.

D   E
Rebel, Rebel, how could they know?

D   E
Hot tramp, I love you so!

Link 1 | D | E | D | E |

| D | E | D | E ||
Doo doo doo, doo doo doo doo doo.

Verse 2

D   E
You've got your mother   in a whirl,
D   E
She's not sure if you're a boy or a girl.
D   E
Hey babe, your hair's all right,
D   E
Hey babe, let's stay out tonight.
D   E
You like me, and I like it all,
D   E
We like dancing and we look divine.
D   E
You love bands when they're playing hard,
D   E
You want more and you want it fast.

Pre-chorus 2

A   D
They put you down, they say I'm wrong.
Bm   E
You tacky thing, you put them on.

Chorus 2

D   E
Rebel, Rebel, you've torn your dress.
D   E
Rebel, Rebel, your face is a mess.
D   E
Rebel, Rebel, how could they know?
D   E
Hot tramp, I love you so!

Link 2 | D | E | D | E |

||: D | E   :||
Doo doo doo, doo doo doo doo.

Chorus 3   As Chorus 2

Link 3 | D | E | D | E   ‖

                D   E

Verse 3   You've torn your dress, your face is a mess.

               D   E
You can't get enough, but enough ain't the test.

                      D   E
You've got your   transmission and your live wire,

                  D   E
You got your   cue line and a handful of 'ludes,

                D   E
You wanna   be there when they count up the dudes.

             D   E
And I love your dress.

               D   E
You're a juvenile success

                   D   E
Because your face is a mess.

           D   E

Outro   So how could they know?

              D   E
I said, how could they know?

                D   E
So what you wanna know? Calamity's child,

             D   E
Chil',   chi-chil', where'd you wanna go?

                D   E
What can I do for you? Looks like you've been there too

                 D   E
'Cause you've torn your dress

              D   E
And your face is a mess,

              D   E
Ooh, your face is a mess,   ooh, ooh.

            D   E
So how could they know?

      D   E
How could they know?

     | D | E | D   ‖

Train In Vain (Stand By Me)

Words & Music by
Mick Jones, Joe Strummer, Paul Simonon & Topper Headon

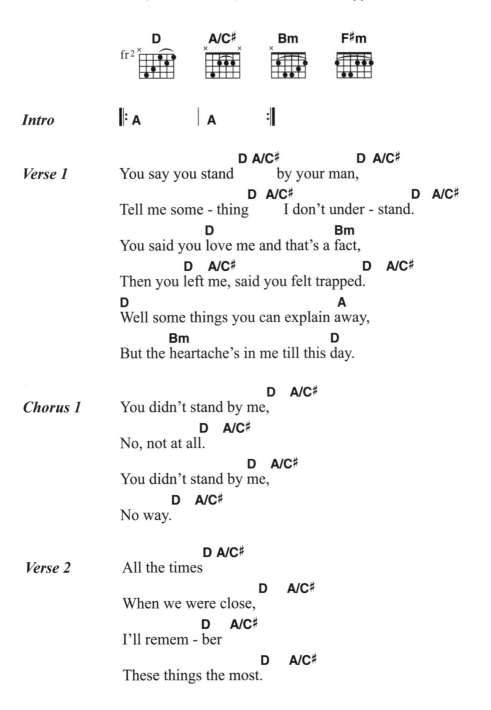

Intro

‖: A | A :‖

Verse 1

                 D A/C#   D A/C#
You say you stand   by your man,

                  D A/C#   D A/C#
Tell me some - thing   I don't under - stand.

                 D   Bm
You said you love me and that's a fact,

             D   A/C#   D   A/C#
Then you left me, said you felt trapped.

D   A
Well some things you can explain away,

          Bm   D
But the heartache's in me till this day.

Chorus 1

                    D A/C#
You didn't stand by me,

          D A/C#
No, not at all.

                  D A/C#
You didn't stand by me,

        D A/C#
No way.

Verse 2

             D A/C#
All the times

                   D   A/C#
When we were close,

         D   A/C#
I'll remem - ber

                  D   A/C#
These things the most.

cont.

      D   **Bm**
I see all my dreams come tumbling down
      D   **A/C♯**   **D**   **A/C♯**
I won't be happy   without you a - round.
     D   **A**
So all alone I keep the wolves at bay,
      Bm   **D**
And there's only one thing that I can say.

Chorus 2

                 D   **A/C♯**
You didn't stand by me,
         D   **A/C♯**
No, not at all.
                D   **A/C♯**
You didn't stand by me,
      D   **A/C♯**
No way.

Bridge

         A   **F♯m**
You must explain____
Bm
Why this must be,

  | **D A/C♯** | **D A/C♯** |
        A   **F♯m**
Did you lie_____
Bm
When you spoke to me?

  | **D A/C♯** | **D A/C♯** |

Chorus 3

               D   **A/C♯**
Did you stand by me?
         D   **A/C♯**
No, not at all.

Verse 3

         D   **A/C♯**
Now I got a job,
           D   **A/C♯**
But it don't pay.
           D   **A/C♯**
I need new clothes,
              D   **A/C♯**
I need somewhere to stay.
      D   **Bm**
But with - out all these things I can do,
            D **A/C♯**   **D** **A/C♯**
But without your love I won't make it through.

cont.

        D   A
But you don't understand my point of view,

        Bm   D
I sup - pose there's nothing I can do.

Chorus 4

                      D   A/C♯
You didn't stand by me,

         D   A/C♯
No, not at all.

                      D   A/C♯
You didn't stand by me,

        D   A/C♯
No way.

                      D   A/C♯
You didn't stand by me,

        D   A/C♯
No, not at all.

                      D   A/C♯
You didn't stand by me,

        D   A/C♯
No way.

Bridge

                A   F♯m
You must explain_____

Bm
Why this must be,

| D A/C♯ | D A/C♯ |

               A   F♯m
Did you lie_____

Bm
when you spoke to me?

| D A/C♯ | D A/C♯ |

Chorus 5

                  D   A/C♯
Did you stand by me?

| D A/C♯ | D A/C♯ | D A/C♯ |

                  D   A/C♯
Did you stand by me?

        D   A/C♯
No, not at all

                  D   A/C♯
Did you stand by me?

           D   A/C♯
No way. :‖

‖: D A/C♯ | D A/C♯ :‖

Substitute

Words & Music by
Pete Townshend

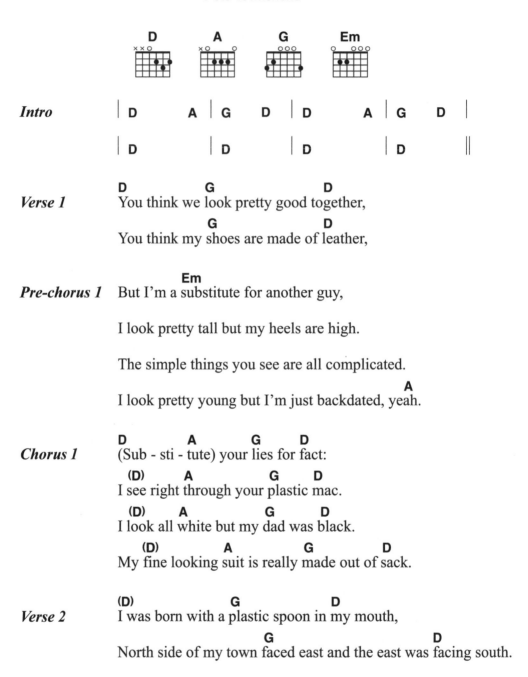

Intro

| D   A | G   D | D   A | G   D |

| D | D | D | D |

Verse 1

D   G   D
You think we look pretty good together,

             G   D
You think my shoes are made of leather,

Pre-chorus 1

            Em
But I'm a substitute for another guy,

I look pretty tall but my heels are high.

The simple things you see are all complicated.

                               A
I look pretty young but I'm just backdated, yeah.

Chorus 1

D   A   G   D
(Sub - sti - tute) your lies for fact:

  (D)   A   G   D
I see right through your plastic mac.

  (D)   A   G   D
I look all white but my dad was black.

    (D)   A   G   D
My fine looking suit is really made out of sack.

Verse 2

(D)   G   D
I was born with a plastic spoon in my mouth,

                G   D
North side of my town faced east and the east was facing south.

Pre-chorus 2
                   Em
And now you dare to look me in the eye

But crocodile tears are what you cry.

If it's a genuine problem you won't try

To work it out at all, just pass it by,

     A
Pass it by.

Chorus 2
D   **A**   **G**   **D**
(Sub - sti - tute) me for him,
(D)   **A**   **G**   **D**
(Sub - sti - tute) my Coke for gin.
(D)   **A**   **G**   **D**
(Sub - sti - tute) you for my mum,
  (D)   **A**   **G**   **D**
At least I'll get my washing done.

Solo
‖: **D** | **G** | **D** | **G** :‖

Pre-chorus 3   As Pre-chorus 1

Link
‖: **D**   **A** | **G**   **D** | **D**   **A** | **G**   **D** :‖

Verse 3   As Verse 2

Pre-chorus 4   As Pre-chorus 2

Chorus 3   As Chorus 2

Chorus 4   As Chorus 1

Wild Wood

Words & Music by
Paul Weller

Bm   Bm9*   Em7   F#7#5b9

*Implied harmony

Intro | Bm | Bm | Bm9 | Bm9 |

              | Em7 | F#7#5b9 | Bm | Bm |

Verse 1

Bm   Bm9
High tide, mid-afternoon,
Em7   F#7#5b9   Bm
People fly by in the traffic's boom.
                      Bm9
Knowing just where you're blowing,
Em7   F#7#5b9   Bm
Getting to where you should be going.

Verse 2

                    Bm9
Don't let them get you down,
Em7   F#7#5b9 Bm
Making you feel   guilty about.
                           Bm9
Golden rain will bring you riches,
Em7   F#7#5b9 Bm
All the good things   you deserve now.

Solo 1 | Bm | Bm | Bm9 | Bm9 |

              | Em7 | F#7#5b9 | Bm | Bm |

Verse 3

Bm   Bm⁹

Bm   **Bm9**
Climbing, forever trying,

Em7   **F#7$_{♭9}^{#5}$** **Bm**
Find your way out of the wild, wild wood.

               Bm9
Now there's no justice,

      Em7   **F#7$_{♭9}^{#5}$**   **Bm**
You've only yourself that you can trust in.

Verse 4

Bm   **Bm9**
And I said, high tide mid-afternoon,

      Em7   **F#7$_{♭9}^{#5}$** **Bm**
Woah, people fly by in the traffic's boom.

               Bm9
Knowing just where you're blowing,

Em7   **F#7$_{♭9}^{#5}$**   **Bm**
Getting to where you should be going.

Solo 2

| **Bm** | **Bm** | **Bm9** | **Bm9** |

| **Em7** | **F#7$_{♭9}^{#5}$** | **Bm** | **Bm** |

Verse 5

Bm   **Bm9**
Day by day your world fades away,

Em7   **F#7$_{♭9}^{#5}$** **Bm**
Waiting to feel all the dreams that say,

             Bm9
Golden rain will bring you riches,

Em7   **F#7$_{♭9}^{#5}$** **Bm**
All the good things   you deserve now, and I say,

Verse 6

             Bm9
Climbing, forever trying

        Em7   **F#7$_{♭9}^{#5}$** **Bm**
You're gonna find your way out of the wild, wild wood.

           Em7   **F#7$_{♭9}^{#5}$**
I said you're gonna find your way out

      Bm
Of the wild, wild wood.

You're Still The One

Words & Music by
Shania Twain & R.J. Lange

G   **C**   **D**   **Am**

Capo eighth fret

Intro | G | G | C | D ||

Verse 1

G
   Looks like we made it,

C   D
Look how far we've come my baby,

G
   We might have took the long way,

C   D
   We knew we'd get there some day.

G   C   D
   They said,   I bet   they'll never make it,

           G   C   D
But just look at us holding on.

                     G   C   D   C
We're still together, still going strong.

Chorus 1

G   C
   You're still the one I run to,

Am   D
   The one that I belong to.

G   C   D   C
   You're still the one I want for life.

G   C
   You're still the one that I love,

Am   D
   The only one I dream of.

G   C   D
   You're still the one I kiss goodnight.

Verse 2

    G
    Ain't nothing better,

C   D
We beat the odds together.

    G
    I'm glad we didn't listen,

C   D
Look at what we would be missing.

    G   C   D
    They said, I bet they'll never make it,

        G   C   D
But just look at us holding on.

              G   C   D
We're still together, still going strong.

Chorus 2

    G   C
    You're still the one I run to,

Am   D
    The one that I belong to.

    G   C   D   C
    You're still the one I want for life.

    G   C
    You're still the one that I love,

Am   D
    The only one I dream of.

    G   C   D
    You're still the one I kiss goodnight.

You're still the one.

Instrumental ‖: G | C | D | D   :‖

Chorus 3

    G   C
    You're still the one I run to,

Am   D
    The one that I belong to.

    G   C   D   C
    You're still the one I want for life.

    G   C
    You're still the one that I love,

Am   D
    The only one I dream of.

    G   C   D
    You're still the one I kiss goodnight.

    G
    I'm so glad we made it,

C   D
Look how far we've come baby.

1 2 3 4 5 6 7 8 9

55

CD TRACK LISTING

1. AMERICA
(BORRELL/BURROWS)
SONY/ATV MUSIC PUBLISHING (UK) LIMITED

2. THE BALLAD OF JOHN & YOKO
(LENNON/MCCARTNEY)
SONY/ATV MUSIC PUBLISHING (UK) LIMITED

3. BEAUTIFUL DAY
(U2)
BLUE MOUNTAIN MUSIC LIMITED

4. BROWN EYED GIRL
(MORRISON)
UNIVERSAL MUSIC PUBLISHING LIMITED

5. COMMON PEOPLE
(COCKER/BANKS/SENIOR/DOYLE/MACKEY)
UNIVERSAL/ISLAND MUSIC LIMITED

6. JAMMING
(MARLEY)
BLUE MOUNTAIN MUSIC LIMITED

7. FAIRYTALE OF NEW YORK
(MACGOWAN/FINER)
UNIVERSAL MUSIC PUBLISHING LIMITED/UNIVERSAL
MUSIC PUBLISHING MGB LIMITED

8. HAND IN MY POCKET
(MORISSETTE/BALLARD)
UNIVERSAL/MCA MUSIC LIMITED

9. I SHOT THE SHERIFF
(MARLEY)
BLUE MOUNTAIN MUSIC LIMITED

10. IN MY PLACE
(BERRYMAN/MARTIN/BUCKLAND/CHAMPION)
UNIVERSAL MUSIC PUBLISHING MGB LIMITED

11. JAILHOUSE ROCK
(LEIBER/STOLLER)
CARLIN MUSIC CORPORATION

12. JOHNNY B GOODE
(BERRY)
JEWEL MUSIC PUBLISHING COMPANY LIMITED

13. LIVE FOREVER
(GALLAGHER)
SONY/ATV MUSIC PUBLISHING (UK) LIMITED

14. LATE IN THE EVENING
(SIMON)
UNIVERSAL/MCA MUSIC LIMITED

15. NAÏVE
(PRITCHARD/HARRIS/RAFFERTY/GARRED)
SONY/ATV HARMONY (UK) LIMITED

16. REBEL REBEL
(BOWIE)
RZO MUSIC LIMITED/EMI MUSIC PUBLISHING LIMITED/
CHRYSALIS MUSIC LIMITED

17. TRAIN IN VAIN
(JONES/STRUMMER/SIMONON/HEADON)
UNIVERSAL MUSIC PUBLISHING LIMITED

18. SUBSTITUTE
(TOWNSHEND)
FABULOUS MUSIC LIMITED

19. WILD WOOD
(WELLER)
UNIVERSAL MUSIC PUBLISHING MGB LIMITED

20. YOU'RE STILL THE ONE
(TWAIN/LANGE)
UNIVERSAL MUSIC PUBLISHING LIMITED/
UNIVERSAL/MCA MUSIC LIMITED